A Science Museum
Booklet

Gas
An Energy Industry

Susan E Messham B Sc

Her Majesty's
Stationery Office
London

ISBN 0 11 290248 0

Acknowledgement

The author is grateful to Dennis Scott Wilson MBE, ARIC, CENG, F I GAS E for reading the manuscript.

Photographs 11, 15, 16, 18, 20, 21, and 22 are reproduced by courtesy of the British Gas Corporation.

Gas: an energy industry

Gas as an energy source

We obtain the energy we need in a variety of different ways, ranging from the conversion of radiant heat and light from the sun into a usable form to the use of earth-bound fuels. Solar energy has its origins in the continuing nuclear reactions which occur on the sun. However, we also have at our disposal other sources of power such as the wind and waves or the gravitational forces which can be seen to operate in tides, dams and waterfalls.

Perhaps the most familiar release of energy is the burning of fuels. These can be of contemporary origin such as wood, but they are more often 'fossil' fuels (so-called because they have lain buried for millions of years and undergone chemical change) such as coal, oil and gas. These fuels may be burnt directly or indirectly. Indirect burning involves the conversion of the substance into another form. Coal for example, may be converted into coal-gas and coke, both of which may be used as fuels.

For many years gas was one of the main fuels for lighting and, though this use eventually declined, it later became increasingly important in heating and cooking. Gas is a very efficient means of storing and distributing energy in a readily usable form, and for nearly 150 years it was produced from coal by various means.

The gas industry remained fundamentally unchanged until the availability of suitable cheap coal declined and the industry switched to oil as its main fuel source. The rate of change was such that by 1965 over 50% of the gas in Britain was being made from oil. When, in the late 1960s, natural gas was discovered under the North Sea, another major technological change began. By 1975 virtually no gas was being made from coal and less than 5% of the total came from oil.

Natural gas is mainly methane, though deposits of other gases such as nitrogen, which are of no use as fuels, have also been found. The gas is located deep beneath the earth's surface and is extracted by means of wells. In Britain the gas is beneath the sea-bed and the extraction is therefore more difficult. 'Town gas' does not occur naturally but has to be manufactured from materials such as coal, oil or wood and, because its main component is hydrogen, it has rather different properties from natural gas.

The type of gas used in various parts of the world depends very much on the local resources and on the economics of transmitting natural gas or gas-making materials from other areas if they are not indigenous. With the discovery of large reserves of natural gas in Holland and under the North Sea, much of Western Europe is changing over from town gas to a natural gas system rather than using the natural gas as a feedstock for the production of town gas. Conversely, in North America, research is being carried out into the production of substitute natural gas from other fuels (especially coal) as a precaution against the ultimate depletion of natural gas wells. In 1970 natural gas accounted for approximately 20% of the world primary energy consumption and this proportion is expected to increase by the end of the century. In addition, some of the primary energy consumption of coal and oil is accounted for in the production of town gas.

The early history of gases
The first scientist to realise that a class of substances similar to air existed apart from atmospheric air was Jan van Helmont (1579–1644), and he called them 'gases'. The Hon. Robert Boyle (1627–91) and John Mayow (1641–79) worked on the handling of gases and introduced greatly improved techniques. Stephen Hales (1677–1761) produced gases which he collected separately from the materials from which he made them. Joseph Priestley (1733–1804) worked on the same idea and by using a trough of mercury succeeded in collecting and identifying several water-soluble gases, like ammonia and hydrogen chloride.

In 1766 Henry Cavendish (1731–1810) prepared a gas by dissolving zinc, iron or tin in sulphuric or hydrochloric acid and he called it 'inflammable air'. This gas was later named hydrogen by Antoine Lavoisier (1743–1794). François Chaussier (1746–1828) stored hydrogen in a bladder and demonstrated how it could be squeezed out through a narrow pipe and ignited. At about the same time Friedrich Ehrmann (1741–1800) suggested that hydrogen could be used for lighting.

These major advances in the techniques for handling gases which were made in the laboratory paved the way for the founding of a gas industry. Without this experience it would have been impossible for the discovery of gas produced from coal to be rapidly developed into an important industry distributing energy to homes and factories.

Naturally occurring inflammable gases sometimes seep from the ground, and in 1618 Jean Tardin investigated burning gas at Grenoble. He thought that the flames were similar to those of burning oil or coal. Later, in 1667, Thomas Shirley (1638–78) described an inflammable gas which came from coal measures near Wigan. The first transmission of natural gas in this country was by James Lowther (1674–1755) who piped fire-damp (methane) from a mine near Whitehaven and burnt it. His agent, Carlisle Spedding, in 1730 offered to light Whitehaven with the gas, carried beneath the streets in pipes, but his offer was refused.

When some coals are heated in the absence of air they break down to liberate gas. Coke and tar are also formed and are sold as by-products. This process is known as the destructive distillation of coal. Coal-gas, prepared by heating coal, was first produced in 1684 by John Clayton (1657–1725). He found that it could be stored in bladders for further use.

Clayton's results were not published until 1739. Meanwhile, in 1727 Hales had found independently that coal gave off an inflammable air on being heated in a closed vessel. The first real advance towards the use of gas for lighting was made by George Dixon (1731–85) who in 1760 heated coal in a kettle and lit the gas at the end of a pipe attached to the kettle spout. He built a pilot plant for the production of 'illuminating gas' but after an explosion he concluded that coal-gas was too dangerous to be used.

In the 1780s Archibald Cochrane, the ninth Earl of Dundonald, built tar ovens to obtain tar from the destructive distillation of coal, and in the process incidentally produced gas which he used to light some rooms in his house, Culross Abbey. The tar was mainly used for caulking ships. Another use for gas was pioneered in 1784 when Jan Minckelers (1748–1824) distilled powdered coal in a gun-barrel and used the gas obtained to fill balloons capable of flight. A year later he is said to have lit his lecture theatre with gas.

Further similar experiments on the production of coal-gas led to individual gas works being installed to light homes and factories. The idea of piping gas from a larger central producing works followed later.

Coal-gas

Although many experiments on the production and use of coal-gas were made in the eighteenth century it was William Murdock (1754–1839) who started the commercial coal-gas industry. Murdock (born Murdoch, he altered the spelling of his name on coming to England from Scotland) generated gas from coal and used it to light a room in his house in Redruth in 1792. He was the first to study gas-making from various types of coal under different conditions. When Murdock moved to Boulton and Watt's Soho factory in Birmingham in 1798 he lit the factory with gas produced in retorts consisting of iron pots, each containing 15 lbs (6.8 kg) of coal.

At about the same time as Murdock was experimenting in England, Philippe Lebon (1767–1804) was producing gas from wood in France. He took out a patent in Paris in 1799 and held public demonstrations in 1801. These demonstrations inspired several inventors to experiment with coal-gas. In 1803, Zachaus Winzler (1750–c1830), who was a Moravian chemical manufacturer, published an account of a method of heating his dining room and cooking by gas, an idea which was years ahead of its time. Another man influenced by Lebon's demonstrations was Friedrich Albrecht Winzer (1763–1830) a German professor of commerce. He had the idea of distributing gas in mains but as he received no support on the continent he came to Britain. On arrival he changed his name to Frederick Winsor and demonstrated lighting by gas in the Lyceum Theatre. Winsor's English was inadequate, so he engaged an assistant to read the lecture while he himself demonstrated the use of gas.

Boulton and Watt's interest in gas lighting revived with increased public awareness of its possibilities, and in 1806 they installed retorts at

1 *Diorama showing Winsor demonstrating gas lighting at the Lyceum Theatre while his assistant reads the lecture (in Science Museum collections)*

the works of Phillips and Lee in Manchester. The firms lighting costs were dramatically reduced and safety was increased. The gasworks installed by Boulton and Watt for various companies were always individual works serving only that particular company. Winsor realised, however, that in the long term this would be impractical and gas would have to be piped under the streets from a larger central gasworks. In order to put his ideas into practice, he tried to form the National Light and Heat Company in 1806 but the company failed to get a government charter. As part of his publicity campaign he lit the south side of the Pall Mall in 1807 with gas piped from his own house. He finally succeeded in 1812 when the Gas Light and Coke Company, a more modest version of his original proposals, gained its charter. Winsor was a poor administrator and the company nearly failed. He resigned and the situation was saved by Samuel Clegg (1781–1861), an engineer who joined the company in 1814. One of Clegg's first achievements was to introduce a method of chemical purification by adding lime to the water in the gasholders and bubbling the gas through it. The lime helped to remove some of the hydrogen sulphide and other sulphur impurities in the gas which gave it an unpleasant smell and which were also poisonous.

By April 1814, gas lighting had been installed in the parish of St Margaret's, Westminster, the gas being produced at a works in Great

2 *Diorama of the gasworks installed by William Murdock at the cotton mills of Phillips and Lee in Manchester in 1807 (in Science Museum collections)*

Peter Street. By May 1815, fifteen miles of mains had been laid in the area and this had increased to twenty-six miles by December. The Great Peter Street works used horizontal cast-iron retorts of circular cross-section which tapered from 12 inches (305mm) diameter to 10 inches (254mm) diameter. These were 10ft (3.05m) long and were closed at one end.

Most of the early retorts were horizontal and, apart from a revolving retort installed by Clegg at the Royal Mint, were all of a similar design. The circular cross-section was changed to elliptical and finally to D-shaped. All these retorts were iron and were soon deformed by the prolonged heating at high temperatures and the setting had to be rebuilt frequently. In order to overcome this problem fire-clay retorts with iron lids were experimentally installed in 1822 but were not generally introduced until 1840. These early retorts were all 'charged' (filled with coal) and 'discharged' (the coke removed) by hand and this process was greatly facilitated by the introduction by George Lowe, in 1831, of the 'through retort' from which the coke produced could be withdrawn at the end opposite to that at which the coal was added. A further advance occurred in 1868 when automatic stoking machines were introduced, although it

5

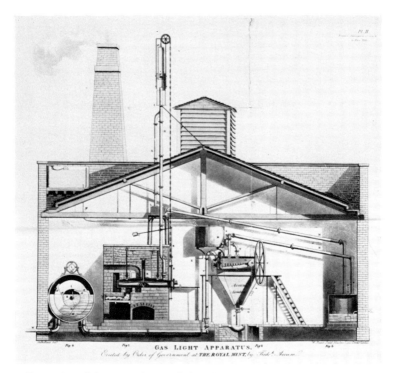

GAS LIGHT APPARATUS.
Erected by Order of Government at THE ROYAL MINT. *by Fredk. Accum.*

3 *Engraving of the gasworks installed at the Royal Mint by Samuel Clegg in 1817*

was many years before hand-charging completely disappeared. These early retorts could only produce gas intermittently because of the need to re-charge at intervals.

An alternative type of retort, the inclined retort, was devised by André Coze of Rheims in 1885. These retorts were inclined at an angle of 32° to the horizontal, enabling charging and discharging to be carried out under gravity. Coal fed by gravity into a retort at that angle formed an even layer along its length. This system also resulted in considerable saving of ground space. As with the horizontal retorts gas production was always intermittent, but the system was widely used for about forty years.

A major advance in the production of gas from coal was the introduction of the vertical retort. The most usual types were continuous in operation, coal being fed in at the top and coke discharged at the bottom, the whole mass moving down the retort under gravity. The coke was cooled by steam at the base of the retort, where the steam reacted with some of the coke to form 'water gas', a mixture of carbon monoxide and hydrogen, which increased the quantity of gas made, but reduced its calorific value. Under optimum conditions continuous vertical retorts could produce $2\frac{1}{2}$ times the output of gas of horizontal retorts on a given land area. An added advantage was that the coke was cool and dry and there was no smoke, dust or steam

6

4 *Charging retorts by hand, 1912*

5 *Charging retorts by machine, 1912*

6 *Clinkering by the old method, 1912*

7 *Discharging coke from the retorts into barrows, 1912*

8 *An Arrol hydraulic gas retort charging machine in a horizontal retort works, 1919*

produced on discharging. A refinement of 1952 improved the efficiency of the plant still further by passing some of the gas produced upwards through the retort to aid the transfer of heat within the retort.

An alternative type of vertical retort, the intermittent vertical retort, was installed at some works. Like the horizontal retort, the coal charge was static in the retort during gas-making, but the coke was steamed during the later stages of gas-making as in the continuous type. The coke was discharged in a mass and replaced by a new charge of coal. An intermittent vertical retort held about 20 tons of coal, whereas an average for a horizontal retort was 15 cwt.

Another method of producing gas from coal was by means of coke ovens. These ovens had been in use for producing coke for metallurgical processes since the early eighteenth century but it was not until 1912 that the gas was collected. This method of producing gas is only economic where the capacity of the ovens exceeds 1000 tons of coal per day. The

process was intermittent and the coke was quenched by water at the end.

All these processes for the production of gas from coal suffer from the disadvantage of needing a large number of labour-intensive purification processes before the gas is suitable for distribution to the customer.

The gas industry at home and abroad

When interest was aroused in lighting by gas in the early nineteenth century it was necessary in Britain to obtain an Act of Parliament if a company with limited liability was to be set up. In 1812 the Gas Light and Coke Company obtained its charter and under it Parliament imposed conditions that the company should supply public lights in streets along which its mains ran at a price cheaper than that of oil, and that it should not sell pipes for taking gas into buildings or stoves to burn it. It was possible, with the consent of the local parish, for non-statutory companies to lay their mains in the same street and there was considerable competition and undercutting of prices. By 1820 fifteen main towns had gasworks and by 1849 the total number of undertakings had risen to nearly seven hundred.

In 1860 the Metropolis Act gave the London companies districts over which they had a monopoly, and the gas was independently tested for purity and pressure. In 1871 these provisions were extended to the whole country.

At the end of the century the supremacy of gas for lighting was challenged by electricity but the introduction of the incandescent mantle prolonged the life of gas as a means of lighting. In 1920 the standardisation

9 *Model of a gasworks in the 1930s* (*in Science Museum collections*)

10 *Cartoon on the laying of gas mains in the early nineteenth century.*
Cruickshank

11 *Beckton Gas Works which produced town gas from coal*

of gas quality was changed from candle-power to calorific value and gas was charged for by the therm (1 therm = 10^5 Btu or $2 \cdot 5 \times 10^4$ Kcal). At this time there were 1,300 gas undertakings in the country, 780 of them statutory, and from then on amalgamation of companies occurred and smaller works ceased to produce gas, their areas being supplied from larger stations.

The development of gas industries throughout the world seems to have followed a very similar pattern. Initially, many small companies were formed, these gradually being grouped into larger companies and finally linked by a nationwide network or networks. The most recent stage in many cases has been the conversion to natural gas necessitating long-distance, high-pressure networks. The exceptions to this pattern are some of the countries with very large reserves of gas associated with oil, many of which have been unable to use more than a minute fraction of the gas locally and have flared most of it. This has happened particularly in the Middle East and in Venezuela although attempts are now being made to set up gas-based industries or to liquefy the gas for export.

EUROPE

Gas lighting was soon introduced into other European countries. Although it had been demonstrated in Paris by Lebon at the end of the eighteenth century, Paris did not have any gas lighting until 1819, and in 1833 there were only 233 lamps in the city. By 1819, Brussels and other Belgian towns were lit by gas. This was followed by the start of the gas industry in Germany in 1824, in Switzerland in 1843 and in Sweden in 1846. Most of the gas was produced from coal, but some gas in Germany and all that in Switzerland was made from wood. When the railway was built to Switzerland in 1847, coal could be imported for gas production but wood continued to play an important rôle in the gas industry. The 1850s were a time of considerable expansion in the gas industry as a whole and gas lighting was introduced into Denmark, Spain, Italy, Poland and Malta, and into Austria in 1864. In some countries considerable rationalization of gas production occurred in the first half of the twentieth century, Belgium in particular setting up a network of long-distance, high-pressure mains principally supplied by coke ovens. Denmark, although possessing many smaller gasworks, supplied most of the country from thirteen works by 1948.

The pattern of gas production was considerably changed by the discovery of natural gas in Europe from about 1940 onwards. By the end of 1973 conversion of appliances was nearly complete in the Netherlands, Belgium, France and Italy and was well advanced in Britain and West Germany.

UNITED STATES OF AMERICA
News of the demonstrations of gas lighting at the end of the eighteenth century soon travelled across the Atlantic and similar experiments were made in the United States. In 1816 gas was produced from tar in Philadelphia and Maryland and in 1817 the first street lamp was lit by coal-gas in Baltimore. In 1821 natural gas was first used to light a few buildings in Fredonia, New York, but natural gas was not used on a large scale for another fifty years. In 1825 a coal-gas company was formed in New York and this was soon followed by other companies throughout the country. By 1839 some 297 companies were serving 4,857,000 people.

Attempts began about 1870 to use the finds of natural gas commercially and by 1880 some areas were using it extensively. Other finds soon followed and for the next thirty years the gas was used indiscriminately, vast amounts being wasted. In the first half of the twentieth century pipelines were built to take natural gas to many other areas of the United States although some coal gas was also produced and used either in isolation or as a mixture with natural gas. Concern about the rate of use of natural gas has led to considerable research being carried out into efficient methods of clean production of gas from coal.

THE REST OF THE WORLD
The gas industry in Canada began in 1847 with the foundation of the Consumers Gas Company of Toronto. In 1861 natural gas was found in Ontario and in 1905 vast quantities were found in Alberta. The country was served partly by town gas and partly by natural gas. In 1948, over half the gas used was natural gas but two thirds of the customers used manufactured gas. In South and Central America there was some development

in the use of coal-gas in the nineteenth century, Rio de Janeiro, Buenos Aires and some parts of Mexico being lit by gas in the 1850s, often under the direction of British engineers. In 1837 the foundation of the Australian Gas Light Company marked the start of the industry in Australia and by 1841 Sydney was lit by gas. In 1856 gas companies were formed to light Melbourne and Hobart, followed by Adelaide in 1863, Brisbane in 1865 and Perth in 1885. The gas was produced mainly from coal from New South Wales but some less suitable brown coal from Victoria was also used. In 1924 natural gas was found in Australia but most of the important finds have been made in more recent years. New Zealand's gas industry started in 1863 and natural gas was discovered there in 1960. Many other parts of the world experimented with gas lighting in the nineteenth century, including Mauritius in the 1850s, Hawaii in 1859, and Hong Kong and Singapore in 1864. In Calcutta the Oriental Gas Company was formed in 1853 and succeeded in lighting the city in 1857, using coal imported from Britain.

Storage and distribution of manufactured gas

The early experimenters with coal-gas and other gases found that small quantities could be stored in bladders for future use. In 1782 Lavoisier used a gasholder which consisted of a cubical bell of metal with its open end submerged in water. This type of holder was adopted by some early gas engineers and used in their installations. However, gasholders were not universally accepted. Winsor disapproved of them, preferring to discharge any excess gas into the air. Gasworks produced gas essentially at a constant rate but initially gas was supplied for lighting only during certain hours of the evening. There was therefore a need to store gas produced during the daytime, if only to prevent considerable wastage. Various types of gasholders were developed, the earlier versions deriving from those in use in laboratories.

There was considerable public concern about the safety of gasholders, and in 1813 a Royal Society deputation recommended that holders should not exceed 6000 cu ft (170 cu m) capacity and should be enclosed in strong buildings. Clegg, of the Gas Light and Coke Company, invited the deputation to the works to demonstrate the safety of gasholders. He struck the bell of the holder with an axe, puncturing the side and then lit the gas which escaped to show that there was no danger of explosion.

By 1816 gasholders were usually cylindrical. The tanks were often brewers' vats, but they suffered from rapid corrosion of the hoops, and brick tanks were soon adopted. These in turn were replaced by cast-iron and steel tanks. The gas entered the holder and the bell rose as a result of gas pressure. The pressure of the gas in the holder was not much higher, however, than atmospheric pressure.

Clegg experimented with other types of holder to try and overcome the problems of building tanks on marshy ground. These were the rotating holder (1815), which incidentally led to the invention of the wet gas meter, and the tent holder (1818), neither of which was particularly successful. Another unsuccessful idea was the use, in 1822, of canvas bags or balloons of 15,000 cu ft (424 cu m) capacity. These were found to be too easily inflammable.

In 1824 Tait devised the telescopic holder, which was a great advance. It enabled more gas to be held on the same land area without increasing the depth of the tank. Early examples were erected at Mile End (London) and Leeds. These holders were surrounded by a braced cast-iron structure which guided their movement. As one lift rises it picks up the next lift, forming a water seal between the two. The next advance in holder design was in 1887 when Pease produced a gasholder which dispensed with the massive surrounding framework, the movement of the holder being guided by weighted wire cables. This type continued in use for many years, and several single lift column-guided holders were enlarged to telescopic holders using wire cables. The spiral-guided holder, which was very widely adopted, was produced by W Gadd and W F Mason in 1887 and the first was erected in 1889 at Northwich. With the exception of one or two early models this type of holder had the great advantage of a completely external mechanism which could be easily maintained. It did not need a heavy and expensive external framework, as the lifts could be guided by runners on the lift below.

All these holders required tanks containing water, and this presented a disposal problem. It also meant drying the gas before transmission. The

12 *Part of a model of a gasworks in the 1930s showing a spiral guided gasholder and a partly-sectioned waterless gasholder* (*in Science Museum collections*)

first waterless holder was invented by Caslon in Britain in 1823, and an improved version was devised by Knapton in 1849, though neither type was ever built. The waterless gasholders erected in Britain in the 1920s were the MAN and Klönne types designed in Germany. With these holders the external structure is rigid and the gas contained beneath a moveable piston inside the holder. Ballast blocks can be placed on top of this piston to regulate the pressure of the gas underneath. The gas is prevented from escaping by a tar seal round the edge of the piston. These holders could be erected quickly and also increased in height (and hence capacity) whilst still in use. The structure itself, with no water seal or subterranean tank, was much lighter than the previous types of holder, but not being telescopic it was a more permanent feature on the skyline.

Water in conventional holders presented problems of freezing in cold weather and of effluent disposal, since the water in the holder absorbed impurities from the gas and had to be renewed periodically. These problems disappeared with the waterless holder, and the drier gas from them caused less corrosion of pipes.

Gas is also stored at high pressure (up to 1000 lb/sq in) in containers in the form of spheres or horizontal cylinders ('bullets') thus enabling more gas to be stored in a given place.

In the earliest gasworks, the holders were marked with accurate graduations so that the volume of gas stored in them could be calculated. This design led to the name *gasometer* being used to describe them, a description that long outlived the type of holder.

The early gas industry consisted of many small works, each with its own gasholders. In many cases after the works were closed gasholders were retained to provide local storage of gas to cope with variations in demand during the day, although the rest of the works had ceased to exist. With the coming of natural gas some local storage was still needed, and telescopic, waterless and high-pressure holders remain in use.

In a gasholder the weight of the descending bell forces the gas from the holder into the mains via an automatic governor which keeps the mains pressure constant. In the days of town gas the works, local holder stations and consumers were linked by a network of pipes. Consumers close to a supply received a gas via a low-pressure main, but for longer distances, medium-pressure feeder mains supplied either local holders or the low-pressure network via a governor. In some areas a high-pressure system linked several gasworks and holder stations over considerable distances as well as feeding the low-pressure mains.

Measurement of gas

Gas first became available for lighting in the home in the early years of the nineteenth century and charges were levied simply on the basis of the time for which gas was available and the number of lights on a particular premises. Supply was limited to certain hours each evening, inspectors being employed by the companies to enforce these restrictions. In general this method was inaccurate, unacceptable and led to frequent abuse.

In 1815 the publisher R Ackermann felt that the method of charging by time was unfair and demanded that he should be charged for his gas by volume. In response to this call, Clegg devised a wet gas-meter but this was found later to be inaccurate due to faulty valves. Two years later Clegg designed an efficient wet meter, one of which was installed at the gasworks at the Royal Mint in 1817. This was the fore-runner of some types of modern meter used as station meters to measure the gas produced in works. John Malam designed an improved wet meter in 1819. By this time gas companies had realised the advantages of measuring the gas supplied and they offered the incentive of a discount of 10% on the price to consumers who agreed to have a meter on their premises.

The London Portable Gas Company, which made gas from whale oil, supplied the gas at 30 atmospheres pressure in copper cylinders of 2 cubic feet capacity. This supply continued until the company failed in 1834.

In the 1830s gas companies were still trying to persuade customers to accept meters and, to prevent the use of gas outside permitted hours, the supply was cut off from sunrise to sunset. About this time there was a new demand for gas for 'stoves' for heating and cooking which required a supply during the day. In order to supply the need a day main was laid in Piccadilly in 1837 and gas was only available from this main via the meters. Other day mains followed, and in 1840 existing mains were used to provide a supply during the day provided that all consumers had meters. This decision by some companies led to their losing customers to other companies still providing an unmetered supply.

The wet meter had a major disadvantage in that the water evaporated and the level had to be maintained between certain specified levels. In 1833 the first dry meter was patented by Miles Berry but it proved unsatisfactory. Alexander Wright's dry meter of 1844 was a considerable improvement and led to dry meters coming into common use by the 1850s. In 1870 T S Lacey patented a meter which delivered a predetermined amount of gas. Although the meter was not adopted it was the forerunner of the slot-meter which was developed in 1887 following a decision to try and widen the market for gas. Although gas apparatus for heating and cooking had been displayed prominently at the Great Exhibition of 1851, it became increasingly popular following the introduction of the prepayment meter.

Gas quality had usually been determined in terms of candle power, which compared the light produced with that obtained from candles. There is now a highly standardised candle. In 1871 it became compulsory for gas to be tested regularly for quality and purity. The gas had to be free of hydrogen sulphide and the pressure supplied had to be maintained at over two inches water gauge (2 inches water gauge = 0·005 atmosphere above atmospheric pressure or 0·07 lb/sq in). As usage of gas for heating increased and that for lighting decreased, the method of standardisation

13 *Caricature 'The Good Effects of Carbonic Gas', 1807*

was changed in 1920 to the maintenance of a defined common calorific value. This marked the change from charging for gas by volume to charging by heat content.

Where large volumes of gas were used by industry, measurement was by a specialized type of wet meter. It had always been a problem both with town gas and natural gas to devise a meter which would measure both the substantial flow of gas for central heating and the relatively minute flow for a pilot light or gas refrigerator. There are three main types of meter in use at the present time, depending on the amount of gas used. The householder uses the positive displacement dry meter, an industrial user has a rotary meter, and metering at the pipeline terminals is by orifice meters. The domestic dry meter consists of two chambers separated by a leather diaphragm. As the chambers alternately fill and empty, the diaphragm is alternately stretched and relaxed, and these movements are transmitted to a counting mechanism which registers the amount of gas passing through the meter. In practice there are two sets of two chambers in each meter.

Using gas

During the nineteenth century the increased availability of gas and the provision of a convenient, relatively efficient form of lighting changed the entire way of life of many people. Roads were adequately lit, and with the almost simultaneous reorganisation of the police force by Sir Robert Peel it became much safer to venture out after dark. The working day in winter was extended, and in the realm of social life it was no longer necessary to have dinner in the middle of the afternoon while there was still sufficient light.

In the earliest experiments with gas lighting the gas was lit directly from the open end of the pipe, with no form of burner. This method was improved by the introduction of burners consisting of iron caps pierced with one or more holes. These burners were known by the shape of the resulting flames, as rat-tail, cockspur or cockscomb. In order to increase the amount of light produced a parabolic reflector was sometimes added. Towards the end of the eighteenth century the Argand burner for oil had

14 *Gas light fittings as illustrated in Fredrick Accum's 'Practical Treatise on Gas-Light' 1815*

been devised using a circular wick to give a tubular flame. In 1809 Clegg adapted this idea for use with gas, the gas issuing from small holes in a circular plate between two concentric brass tubes. These burners required glass chimneys to ensure proper air supply.

A notable advance was the invention, in 1816, of the batswing burner by Winsor's assistant, Stone. This burner was simple and efficient and was generally adopted for street lamps. In 1820, a type of burner was invented which did not really achieve its potential for another hundred years. This was the union jet, invented by James Neilson and James Milne of Glasgow. In this burner two equal jets of gas were allowed to impinge on one another to produce a flat flame of increased efficiency.

The amount of light produced by these early burners was often quite small and it depended on the composition of the gas as well as on the burner design. It was necessary with this type of burner to use gas which contained longer chain or unsaturated hydrocarbons as impurities, since these compounds burn incompletely and give a yellow colour in the flame. With this idea in mind Lowe devised a lamp in which naphtha vapour was burnt in conjunction with the gas to improve the light produced. This lamp was first shown at the Great Exhibition of 1851.

An important advance was made by William Sugg in 1858. He found that burners could be made from steatite (soapstone) which was heat-treated, shaped, boiled in oil to colour it, and finally polished. These burners were much more easily regulated and did not have the dis-advantage of the metal ones which tended to deform with the heat of the flame. They gave a better flame as heat was not conducted away by the burner. The original type of burner relied entirely on the gas mixing with enough air in the flame to burn satisfactorily. In 1840 a burner was designed in which air entered and mixed with the gas below the point of combustion and this resulted in a hotter flame, less soot and more heat per unit time. This was preceded by Faraday's work on the forerunner of the 'Bunsen' burner which consisted of a tube with an open funnel below it and a gas jet within it.

Gas burners soon became popular in laboratories, and in 1852 Sonnen-schein used burners and a gas furnace for organic combustions in his laboratory. The advent of coal-gas to Heidelberg in 1853 led Robert Bunsen to experiment with a laboratory burner. This burner was a modifi-cation of the Argand burner brought to Heidelberg by Henry Roscoe and was described in a joint paper in 1857. It formed the basis of many later applications of gas lighting and heating, both in laboratory and domestic use and was not superseded until the 'neat' or flat flame burner was intro-duced for gas fires in the 1930s. This so-called 'neat' flame burner worked on the same principle as the union jet invented over a hundred years earlier.

In 1884 Carl Auer was working in Bunsen's laboratory on the properties of rare earths when he noticed that a solution of the compounds, spilt on an asbestos sheet, gave an intense glow in a gas flame. Auer experimented with various salts to produce an impregnated fabric which could be used to make this glow. His first incandescent mantle consisted of a mixture of 60% zirconium oxide, 20% lanthanum oxide and 20% yttrium oxide. This was later changed to a mixture of thorium and cerium oxides. In recognition of his achievements Auer received the degree of Doctor of Philosophy and was given the title 'Carl Auer von Welsbach' by the Austrian Government.

The early mantles of about 1887 were not very efficient and they were extremely fragile. They were expensive at five shillings each, and the burner had to be returned to the manufacturer whenever a new mantle was needed. The quality of the mantles improved over the years, however, and they were first tried out in street lighting in London in 1895. The discovery of the incandescent gas mantle came at a most fortuitous time in the history of gas lighting. Its introduction enabled gas lighting to hold its own against increasing competition from electricity in the last years of the nineteenth and first years of the twentieth centuries.

With almost all gaslight fittings much of the light was lost, as it was given out above the level of the burner and was often inadequately reflected from the walls and ceiling. In 1897 Kent devised a burner in which it was possible to invert the mantle and hence greatly improve the light. This idea was taken up by other workers, mainly in Europe, and finally perfected, the first domestic version appearing in 1909 and a version for street lighting in 1910. Another invention designed to increase the convenience of gas lighting was the gas burner switch which enabled gaslights to be switched on at a distance with the same ease as electric lights.

In the early years of the twentieth century electric lighting improved and the use of gas lighting began to decline. The output of gas was inferior to electric light but many people preferred gas lighting on aesthetic grounds. Gas lighting survived the longest in its use in street illumination, with the lamplighter largely giving way to the pilot light and time clock. In 1933 the streets of London contained approximately equal numbers of gas and electric lights. Gas-lights could still be seen in certain areas of London in 1975 (eg, Covent Garden) while Birmingham's last four gas-lights were replaced on 3 January 1975. In the 1970s mantles are still in use in, for example, caravans and boats and on building sites with a 'bottled gas' (propane or butane) supply.

In the early years of gas supply gas was used almost exclusively for lighting, although experiments were made to use it for heating or cooking. The Moravian chemical manufacturer, Zachaus Winzler, gave dinner parties in December 1802 at which the dining room was heated by gas and the food cooked on a gas stove He published an account of his experiments in 1803. The cooker consisted of four burners and a small oven below them.

The first mention of the use for gas for cooking in this country was in the Mechanics Magazine in 1831. There was a problem, to begin with, that in general gas supplies were not metered and the use of gas was prohibited during the day. Increasing demand from customers wanting to use it outside these hours led to the laying of day mains in certain streets, and eventually to the compulsory metering of all customers. In 1841, gas was installed for cooking at the London Reform Club, and in the following years many types of cooker were designed, some later ones benefitting greatly from the discovery of the bunsen burner in the 1850s. At the 1851 Great Exhibition, at which several cookers were exhibited, the Jury reported that they '. . . refer to these contrivances less for their present completeness and efficiency than for their probable future importance, which, some of its members believe, can hardly be overestimated'. Gradual improvements to cookers were made over the years, perhaps the most significant of which was the introduction of the gas oven thermostat in 1923. The forerunner of the modern gas ring was introduced in 1867.

The idea of heating water for domestic use by gas dates back to the middle of the nineteenth century. In about 1850 a bath was produced in which both water and bath were heated by gas jets underneath. In 1868 Benjamin Maugham invented the 'geyser' to heat water as it flowed into the bath, but the early geysers were highly dangerous as they had no flue. The efficiency and safety of these devices were gradually improved, and in the 1930s automatic lighting from a pilot light was introduced.

Although it was near the end of the nineteenth century before a really acceptable gas fire was designed, attempts to heat rooms by gas had been made over many years. In 1799 Philippe Lebon patented his 'Thermolampe' in France, which combined lighting and heating but which also, due to lack of purification of the gas, produced an unpleasant smell. This discouraged its adoption.

Space heating by gas fire was first suggested by John Maiben in 1813, who advocated gas-flames playing on 'fancy-figures' of cast metal. The main problem in the development of gas fires was the selection of a suitable material to form the radiants to propagate the energy of the flame into the area to be heated. Pumice balls were tried by Edwards in 1849 and in 1851 Smith and Phillips produced a fire imitating a coal fire using glass and firebrick. In 1852 Goddard invented asbestos fibre and a firebrick back was introduced in 1859. In 1882 Leoni combined these features to produce the first really successful gas fire. This fire provided heat by thermal radiation from a back consisting of firebrick in which tufts of asbestos were embedded. It used an adaptation of a Bunsen burner to give a hotter flame than had been possible before premixing was introduced.

Columnar radiants were introduced in 1905 and the familiar grid form of columnar fireclay radiants in 1925. The first major change in burner design since the introduction of the Bunsen burner was the use of the 'neat' flame in the 1930s which gave the performance of a premix flame without the noise of the air being drawn in.

A significant advance in gas fire design was made in the mid 1950s when the 'convector' gas fire was introduced. This enabled much of the heat previously lost up the flue to be used to warm up the room by means of a heat exchanger. The great improvement in efficiency made a significant contribution to easy implementation of the Clean Air Act of 1956.

The uses of gas have changed dramatically since its introduction. At that time the new superior form of lighting revolutionised the everyday life of many people, but now very little interest is taken in it. Modern uses of gas are all geared to the efficient release of energy in the form of heat rather than light. As a fuel it has wide applications in industrial processes, typical examples of which are bread-baking, pottery firing, heat-treatment of metals, baking of enamels, glass heating, extrusion of plastics, grass drying, cable sheathing, and electric light-bulb manufacture. It can also be used in total energy schemes for providing power, light, hot water, space-heating, refrigeration and air-conditioning for industrial or commercial complexes, the electricity being produced by a gas turbine driving a generator.

Gas, not just coal-gas

Before natural gas was discovered off the coast of Britain, the production of fuel gases from a variety of raw materials had been investigated. The processes involved often differed considerably from the continuous vertical retort coal-gas plant. Conventional coal gasification using bituminous coal produces a mixture of combustible gases, noncombustible gases (such as nitrogen and carbon dioxide) and impurities (including water, tar and sulphur compounds). The production of gas by these methods is labour intensive, the gas requiring extensive purification. The raw material is slow and cumbersome to handle and efficiency of the process requires good quality coal and a ready market for coke.

By the mid 1960s the reserves of good quality coal for gas-making were diminishing, and in order to cope with seasonal fluctuations in demand a secondary method of producing gas at short notice was required. Carburetted water gas had already become an important back-up method of production at times of peak demand. Carburetted water gas was a mixture of water gas made from the action of steam on white hot coke and gas made by spraying oil on to hot bricks. Water gas itself has a low calorific value but after blending with the gas produced from oil the resulting carburetted water gas has the same calorific value as normal town gas.

New methods for gasifying coal which is unsuitable for coke production (eg, brown coal) were investigated especially in countries lacking good coking-coal. In 1861, William Siemens' gas producer completely gasified non-coking coals by passing steam and air through beds of coal. The gas produced was of low calorific value and the method could not be used for coking bituminous coals.

In 1889 Ludwig Mond devised a process to produce ammonia from coal. The coal was heated with air and steam to give a mixture of gases. The ammonia was removed in the form of ammonium sulphate after treatment of the gases with sulphuric acid. The remaining fuel gas was of low calorific value but suitable for many industrial uses. The process could be adapted to use peat or brown coal as well as harder coals. Plants were installed throughout the country and abroad, including several in Japan and some in America. This process was still in use in Staffordshire in 1956, supplying local industry.

Several other attempts were made to devise a successful means of complete gasification of coal both in this country and abroad. Tully, in 1919, introduced a method in which carbonisation took place in the second stage of the so-called 'double gas' plants, the process heat being supplied from a coke gasification (water gas) first stage. Coke formed in the second stage was used as fuel for the first stage, thereby completing the gasification of the coal. In 1958 about fifty of these plants were in operation in Britain. The disadvantages of these and similar types of complete gasification were the comparatively poor thermal efficiency (60%) and gas of rather low calorific value, although the Tully plants were associated with oil carburetting to increase the fuel calorific values of the gas.

Coal for the production of gas by conventional means was becoming increasingly expensive as stocks were depleted, and a process of gas-making which used brown coal or other non-coking coals began to become attractive in the 1950s. The process originated in the late 1920s in Germany when the firm of Lurgi carried out experiments on the complete gasification of brown coal. The first Lurgi plant was built in 1936 and was soon followed by others. Since then considerable work has been carried out by

15 *Westfield Development Centre which was built originally for producing town gas by the Lurgi process*

the British gas industry to adapt the process to the quite different conditions required for British black coals. The coal is subjected to steam and oxygen at high pressure and about two thirds of the original therms are produced as gas, the only residue being ash. The gas produced is of rather low calorific value (400 Btu/cu ft, 3572 Kcal/cu m) although considerably better than that produced by previous methods of complete gasification.

The first Lurgi plant to be built in Britain was at Westfield, in Scotland, using open-cast coal mined nearby. This was followed by a larger plant at Coleshill and a further plant was planned. However, the Coleshill plant closed early in 1969 after only five years operation and the Westfield plant is now used as an experimental station for the production of substitute natural gas.

The Lurgi process did not prove to be competitive with the new oil gasification processes developed by the British gas industry in their West Midlands Research Station, which then came into full commercial production. The Lurgi process needed oxygen which was expensive, and it required large quantities of steam producing very large quantities of weak ammonia liquor, which had to be disposed of after costly treatment. Furthermore, with relatively cheap oil fractions easily available from the refineries, even the cost of low grade coal was uneconomic.

As early as 1868 Sir William Siemens conceived the idea of the gasification of coal underground. This would make large amounts of coal available for gas-making, which would not be economic to mine. In 1914 Sir William Ramsay made some small-scale trials in Durham but there was no further work in this country until 1950. Prior to this large-scale trials had been made by the Russians as far back as the 1930s, and elsewhere in Europe in the late 1940s. The expected usefulness of underground gasification has in general not been realised in practice. The main trials in this country did not use boreholes directly from the surface but those driven off an underground gallery. Pipes were inserted into the borings, air pumped through an inner pipe and the gas produced emerged between two pipes. The trials succeeded in producing gas but only of low calorific value. More significantly, the calorific value decreased steadily as production continued, until eventually the gas would not burn at all and at best was only suitable for gas-turbine fuelling.

In the 1960s great emphasis was placed on the production of gas from oil, but in the United States there was growing awareness of the limited reserves of oil and gas as compared with coal. This awareness led to more research into the efficient production of gas from coal, particularly using entrainment-gasification. This process uses finely pulverised coal which is passed through the gasifier at high temperatures suspended by the mixture of air (or oxygen), steam and product gases. A clean gas of low calorific value is produced which is useful for firing the boilers of electricity generating stations. This was one of several different processes for the clean gasification of coal under trial in the USA by 1974. The calorific value of the gas produced ranged from just over 100 to almost 1000 Btu/cu ft depending upon the conditions used.

Research by the British gas industry led to a full-scale pilot plant for a modified Lurgi process, in which molten slag was produced to obviate the need for large amounts of steam. Research was also carried out into the production of town gas by high-pressure gasification of coal. Until the advent of natural gas from the North Sea, however, the cheapest way of making town gas was from light distillate oil (naphtha).

Coal was the major raw material for the production of gas for over a century and a half, until it was overtaken by oil and finally by natural gas. Oil from various sources, however, had been used to produce gas from the very early days of the gas industry. When gas was first introduced for lighting, whale oil interests regarded it as a potential threat to the survival of oil lighting and they went into competition with gas produced from whale oil of which they had guaranteed supplies. In about 1815 John and Philip Taylor invented a process for the production of gas from whale oil but this failed due to the sooting of the metal vessels. Most of the early companies using oil as a raw material failed by the mid 1830s.

Towards the end of the nineteenth century Alfred Mansfield marketed a plant which his company's letterhead proclaimed as a 'patent plant for making cheap gas from oil, sawdust, nut shells, mineral, vegetable and animal matter.' The oil was heated in a retort and the gas produced purified before being stored in a conventional gasholder. Some early work on the production of gas from oil was done by T S Lowe who in 1874 devised a method of spraying oil on to the surface of hot coke or brick to give a gas of high calorific value. Lowe's main aim in experimenting with this rich gas was to enrich water gas which was produced as part of the same cycle. This mixture became known as carburetted water gas, a particularly valuable means of producing gas quickly to meet peak demand.

As the petroleum industry developed during this century the refineries started producing a surplus of 'refinery gas' and also feedstock suitable for the production of gas from oil. Many different processes were devised to make gas of almost any calorific value, and by the early 1960s these were in commercial operation. The development of processes for the production of gas from oil was linked very closely with parallel developments in the chemical industry, and it is impossible to consider the gas industry in isolation from the rapidly expanding chemical industry.

The continuous catalytic reforming process was originally developed by ICI for making hydrogen for ammonia synthesis. It consisted of reacting purified light distillate oil (naphtha) with steam over a catalyst at 20–30 atmospheres, and at a temperature of 700–900°C. The resulting gas was rich in hydrogen and hence was a 'lean' gas of low calorific value. It was generally enriched by the addition of liquid petroleum gas or rich gas from a different process. Plants of this type were built at Hythe, Kent and Bromley-by-Bow, London, among other places. The process had the great

16 *Reforming plant for the production of town gas from naphtha and natural gas at Hitchin, Herts*

advantage that a considerable flexibility of feedstock was possible and it was later used to produce town gas from natural gas before appliances were converted to burn natural gas.

The catalytic rich gas process was developed by the British gas industry to produce a rich gas of calorific value 500–950 Btu/cu ft (4470–8490 Kcal/ cu m). In this method the same basic processes were used as in the previous method but operation at lower temperatures (500–550°C), and the use of less steam, favoured the production of methane. The methane produced was either converted to town gas or employed as substitute natural gas or used to enrich lean gases produced by other processes. This process is particularly popular in the United States where there was great interest in a process which could be used to provide substitute natural gas, and more than a dozen plants have been erected in the United States under licence from the British gas industry.

A third process, the gas recycle hydrogenator, was also developed by the British gas industry to produce gas without the use of catalysts or steam. Naphtha was reacted with hydrogen at 750°C and at 20–30 atmospheres pressure in a vessel (a 'hydrogenator') in which the products were recirculated. The gas produced consisted mainly of methane and ethane and was therefore of high calorific value, and could be used to enrich the lean gas made in a continuous catalytic reformer, part of the lean gas being used as the hydrogen for the gas recycle hydrogenator.

The use of oil as a feedstock for the production of gas has many advantages over the older type of coal carbonisation. Much more sophisticated chemical engineering methods can be used with liquid or gaseous feedstocks, the plant occupies a smaller area and its capital cost is considerably less. A wide range of gases can be produced and carbon monoxide can be largely eliminated so that the gas is essentially non-toxic. In the traditional production of gas from coal considerable purification of the gas was needed and several by-products were produced including coke, so that the industry was a two-fuel industry. Oil gasification produces gas only, and there are no by-products. The production of the gas at high pressures reduces transmission costs and enables gas to be piped over much greater distances without costly boosting.

The change from coal to oil for gas-making was a major technological revolution in an industry which had remained fundamentally unchanged for nearly 150 years. With the discovery of North Sea gas in the late 1960s another major change took place so that by 1975 less than 5% of the total gas produced was made from oil.

In recent years particular emphasis has been placed on the efficient conversion of one form of stored energy into another. At the same time there has been a growing awareness of the undesirability of pollution, and attempts have been made to eliminate any possible source of pollutants in the production and consumption of gas. The use of waste products for the preparation of fuel gases has so far had very limited application, except in time of war. An alternative source of methane is the fermentation of sewage, and in the Greater London area the pumping engines at some sewage works are powered by methane obtained from sewage. Extending this idea in 1973 the Ministry of Agriculture, Fisheries & Food investigated the possibility of obtaining methane from pig manure. These sources of energy may be of great significance in the future, both contributing to the disposal of waste and helping to conserve energy.

Natural gas

Since the 1950s two major changes have taken place in the choice of raw material for gas production. In the first place cheap oil became available and for a time it was the principal source of gas. Then in 1959 the first liquefied natural gas was imported into this country to be used either for conversion to town gas or to enrich 'lean' gases produced from oil. The discovery, in 1965, of gas under the North Sea dramatically changed the whole basis of the gas industry. Here, for the first time, was a gas occurring naturally which, after minor treatment, could be delivered directly to the customer provided that the gas appliances had been 'converted' for its use. Natural gas had been known and used for many years in other parts of the world, but its advent to Britain altered the whole pattern of gas production and total gas consumption in this country trebled over the first ten years of North Sea gas being supplied.

In Britain seepages of methane associated with coal gave rise to myths of burning springs. Some of these were investigated as far back as the seventeenth century, and it was shown that the phenomenon was, in fact, due to the seepage of gas near the spring. In other parts of the world, especially the Middle East, natural gas seepages which were ignited by lightning often burnt for centuries.

The Chinese are thought to have found natural gas as early as the third century AD and to have piped it through bamboo pipes for use in evaporating brine. Apart from some local uses of natural gas for lighting in Northern Italy from the seventeenth century onwards, the first commercial application in modern times was in America. In 1820 William Hart drilled a shallow well at Fredonia in New York State and piped the gas to several local buildings, but it was the discovery of gas in Pennsylvania in the 1860s which led to the beginning of the first large-scale distribution of natural gas for lighting and heating. It was not until the discovery of the Slochteren gas field in the Netherlands in 1959 that the natural gas industry in Western Europe really began to develop on a large scale.

In this country as long ago as 1730 an offer was made to light Whitehaven, Cumbria, with gas piped from a colliery but this was refused. Nearly 200 years later, in 1957, methane was drained from a colliery in Staffordshire and mixed with coal-gas from a nearby gasworks before delivery. This scheme was extended to include at least three other collieries. It had the advantage of both using gas which would otherwise be wasted and improving conditions within the mines. In 1869 the first onshore natural gas in Britain was found when a well was being drilled at Heathfield in Sussex to search for water. The gas was used to light the local railway station, but although a total of seven wells were drilled, the last in 1955, there was insufficient gas produced to warrant further development.

Natural gas was discovered in two places in Britain in 1938 but no commercial outlet existed at the time and the wells were sealed. In 1957 the gas at Cousland in Scotland came into use; it was piped to the gasworks at Musselburgh and formed part of the town gas supply. In 1959 the gas at Eskdale near Whitby was purchased by the North Eastern Gas Board to be reformed for delivery as town gas.

Liquid natural gas was first imported into Britain in 1959. It came from the Gulf of Mexico where it was liquefied and then transported on a specially converted tanker, 'Methane Pioneer', to Canvey Island, Essex. The liquid gas occupies only 1/600th of the volume occupied by the gaseous form and, provided that a low enough temperature ($-161°C$) is maintained, the liquid may be kept at atmospheric pressure. On reaching Canvey Island the liquefied gas is piped ashore in an insulated pipeline and stored as a liquid until required. When the scheme first started the natural gas had to be converted to town gas before distribution. From Canvey Island a new grid was laid to transport methane gas to as many of the Area Boards as possible. The grid reached as far north as Leeds and served eight of the twelve Area Boards. This grid was of great importance when North Sea gas was first produced as it provided a backbone for the necessary countrywide distribution of natural gas following conversion.

The success of the 'Methane Pioneer' led to the building of specially-designed tankers to carry liquefied natural gas from Algeria to Britain. These tankers were powered by dual-fired engines, the slight boil-off of gas from the cargo accounting for 30% of the fuel used, the remainder being oil. The gas was piped from the field to Arzew, a port on the Algerian coast, liquefied there, and loaded into tankers. The gas from Canvey was either converted into town gas by reforming processes or used to enrich 'lean' gases made from oil.

Natural gas may either be found alone (unassociated) or with oil (associated). The gas in the North Sea and in Western Europe is mainly unassociated and probably originated in very deeply buried coal seams, the gas migrating upwards until stopped by impermeable rock. In many parts of the world and in particular the Middle East and Venezuela, the gas is found associated with oil, and it is impossible to produce the oil without obtaining large amounts of gas. In many cases these oil wells are in areas where there is little or no demand for natural gas as a fuel and the gas is wasted by being flared (burnt). It is sometimes feasible to reinject at least some of the gas to pressurize the oil well and this is generally encouraged wherever possible. The total world reserves of natural gas cannot be accurately known as the search for oil and gas continues all the time. Some vast fields have been discovered in areas such as Alaska, Siberia, and Northern Australia where exploitation is difficult and where there is a negligible local market for the gas. With a continuing increase in the world demand for energy there has been a considerable expansion of the transport of natural gas by tanker and long-distance, high-pressure pipeline from distant fields to the consumer.

In Western Europe natural gas was discovered in France in 1939 and in Italy in 1944 and this gas was used locally. It was in 1959 that, when a very large natural gas field was discovered at Slochteren, in the Netherlands, the European natural gas industry really began on a large scale. The discovery of this field encouraged further exploration, particularly in the

North Sea. The first gas to be found under the North Sea was the West Sole field, in 1965, and this was soon followed by the discovery of other fields. The indigenous natural gas in Europe is supplemented by gas piped from the Soviet Union. There are plans to serve Austria, West Germany, Italy and possibly France with Russian gas in the future. The Soviet Union has probably the largest reserves of natural gas in the world, most of the gas being found east of the Urals and used to the west of them. The rest of Eastern Europe has only very small reserves and much of the gas used there is imported from the Soviet Union.

In North America the United States has considerable reserves of natural gas but recently demand has been exceeding new discoveries. There have been suggestions that a higher price should be charged for the gas to encourage exploration by American companies at home rather than in other parts of the world. Some of the gas from Alaska is liquefied and exported to Japan but gas is also imported to the United States from Canada and Mexico where considerable reserves of gas are known.

In South America most of the known reserves of natural gas are associated with oil. There is no international gas pipeline and owing to the lack of transport facilities and home markets a large amount of the gas produced with oil is wasted. In 1970, 10% of the gas was sold, 10% was used in the extraction of liquid petroleum gas, 40% was reinjected for maintaining pressure in the wells and the remaining 40% was flared to waste. The situation has improved since then, more gas is being reinjected and the local market for gas is increasing.

Natural gas has been imported from Africa, particularly from Algeria, to Britain for some years. Both associated and unassociated gas is found in North Africa but only Algeria and Libya export liquid natural gas on a large scale. Prior to this development 80% of the gas produced in Libya was probably flared. In many other African countries no local markets exist, and this has led to considerable wastage. The gas found in the Middle East is largely associated with oil, the main reserves known in 1975 being in Iran and Saudi Arabia, lesser amounts being found in Kuwait and Iraq. This caused something of a problem as there was little local demand for the gas which was necessarily produced with oil. Some gas was re-injected but vast amounts still needed to be flared. The seriousness of this wastage is generally appreciated and great efforts are being made to set up gas-based chemical industries. Plans are also being considered for the export of liquid natural gas, mainly to Japan.

Pakistan, India and Bangladesh have considerable reserves of gas, while estimates of gas reserves in China, necessarily conjectural, suggest they are probably vast. Japan has small amounts of natural gas and is also the major market for Indonesian gas. There are large reserves of natural gas in Australia, recent finds in the Northern Territory being rather inaccessible. Gas has also been found in New Zealand and is being used locally. It contains an unusually high percentage (44%) of carbon dioxide.

These discoveries of large world reserves of natural gas have been very important in the planning of energy programmes. For the first time gas was available worldwide as a primary energy source without the unavoidable energy loss incurred in the conversion of other fuels such as coal and oil to gas.

Exploration

Natural gas may be found associated with either coal or oil, or apparently unassociated. However, gas found by itself has probably migrated upwards from its point of formation, where it would very possibly have been formed in association with oil or coal. The exception is in cases of very old and hence often very deep gasfields. The deeper that oil has been buried and hence the longer it has been forming, the lighter the molecules of hydrocarbons present are, and the greater the likelihood that several of the constituents will be gaseous.

Oil is formed by the accumulation of marine organisms on the sea bed. These deposits become mixed with inorganic molecules from the sea and eventually get buried under further deposits. As they are compacted the combined action of bacteria and the catalytic effect of the inorganic substances on the marine organisms at high pressure cause the production of hydrocarbons. The more deeply the deposits are buried the further the decomposition proceeds and the lighter the final constituents of the oil. Oil and gas formed in this way are very rarely found where they were formed. They migrate upwards and sideways through porous rock until they eventually escape at the surface unless contained beneath a suitable impervious cap rock. The alternative means of formation of natural gas is from vegetable origins. In a similar way to oil formation, vegetable matter accumulated in swamps and mixed with inorganic sediment became buried and gradually compressed. Coal and associated gas were formed in this way and also on occasions oil. As with the formation of oil reservoirs, the natural gas migrated upwards from the layer where it was formed until trapped by impervious cap rock. The rock which forms the reservoir for the oil or gas is porous, up to 30% of the volume of the rock being pore space. These pores may either be filled with oil or gas or with water, the former two replacing the latter as the reservoir is formed. When oil or gas is drawn off no large hole is left in the rock, as the water comes back into the reservoir to fill the minute pores in the rock vacated by the oil or gas. In order for gas or oil to be trapped underground there must be the right geological structure to form a reservoir which the gas can enter from below but be unable to escape from. There are a number of different formations which can lead to oil or gas being trapped, the general requirements being a completely impervious cap rock surmounting a porous layer of rock.

The North Sea area has been in a position over the years to trap gas produced both from coal and from marine organisms. In carboniferous times

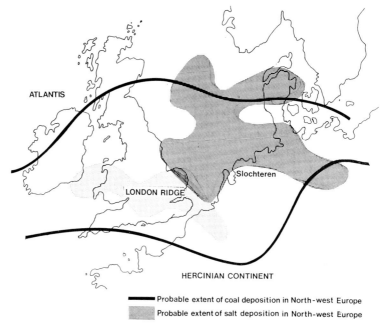

ATLANTIS

LONDON RIDGE

Slochteren

HERCINIAN CONTINENT

■ Probable extent of coal deposition in North-west Europe
▨ Probable extent of salt deposition in North-west Europe

17 *Map illustrating the source of the gas found under the North Sea*

(350 million years ago) the area of the North Sea mainly consisted of lagoons and swamps ideal for the formation of coal. The area was gradually filled in with sediment from adjacent land masses, and by early Permian times (270 million years ago) it was land and the Rotliegendes sandstone was being formed. By late Permian times (225–250 million years ago) part of Northern Western Europe was again flooded by a shallow sea and lakes. Many of these lakes evaporated leaving a thick salt deposit, and it is this which trapped the gas produced with the coal in the Rotliegendes sandstone. For many years the North Sea continued as a sedimentary basin and the marine deposits led to the formation of oil and gas above the major gas deposits derived from coal.

Deductions may be made about the likelihood of finding oil or gas reservoirs in any particular part of the world, but considerable exploration is then required to determine if any deposits actually exist. On land a definite indication of the presence of oil or gas is the seepage to the surface of one or other. This indicates leakage of a reservoir which is sometimes found to be severely depleted but in other cases is worth investigating. These seepages range from comparatively small amounts of gas to 'asphalt lakes' such as the Trinidad Pitch Lake. Early oil prospecting consisted almost entirely of detecting seepages and then drilling nearby. This era was followed by a search for anticlines, as judged by the surface contours, and drilling as near the crest as possible. The disadvantages of this

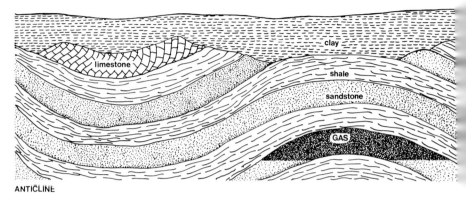

A

limestone
clay
shale
sandstone
GAS

ANTICLINE

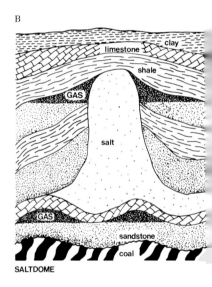

B

limestone clay
shale
GAS
salt
GAS
sandstone
coal

SALTDOME

C

clay
limestone
shale
GAS
sandstone

FAULT

method were that the geological structure underground was not necessarily mirrored by the surface contours and also that there was often no clear indication of how deep the oil or gas was likely to be if indeed it existed at all. The use of aerial photography has greatly improved the accuracy of these overall surveys.

Nowadays geophysical surveys are always carried out before drilling. There are three main types of geophysical survey; gravity survey, seismic survey and magnetic survey. The gravity survey takes into account slight variations in the earth's gravitational field due to the denser or lighter rocks beneath the surface. Measurements are quick to make and although interpretation is not straight forward, useful indications of buried rock

D

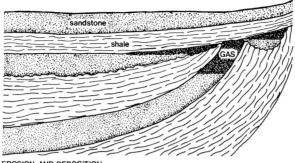

EROSION AND DEPOSITION

E

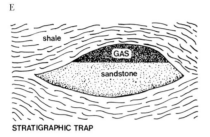

STRATIGRAPHIC TRAP

A *The dome-like shape of the anticline ensures that gas migrating upwards from a suitable source material collects in the pores of the rock beneath the top of the impervious dome.*

B *Anticlines are usually formed by folding of the rock structure due to lateral pressures, but they can also be formed by the upward thrust of molten salt. This forms a 'salt dome', which can protrude into a porous layer to form a suitable gas or oil reservoir round the top of the salt. The salt dome can also distort higher layers of rock to form an anticline structure above it.*

C *Faulting can also form traps capable of containing oil or gas. When layers of rock are moved relative to each other it is possible for a section of porous rock through which gas is migrating to be blocked off by impervious rock and the gas to be trapped.*

D *A further method of forming reservoirs arises from the deposition of impervious rock on top of much older rocks which have been tilted and eroded leading to sloping layers of porous rock being capped by the new impervious rock.*

E *Stratigraphic traps containing oil or gas are formed essentially by sedimentation, an area of porous rock which may contain oil or gas being trapped between two layers of impervious rock so that the hydrocarbons cannot escape.*

formations may often be obtained from these measurements. This type of survey is more difficult at sea than on land due to wave effects, and submarines are often used. Magnetic variations in the earth's crust can be measured and give some indication of the presence of deep-seated arching of basement rocks which could give rise to anticlines of oil or gas bearing rock above.

Seismic surveying depends on the fact that the waves resulting from an explosion near the earth's surface travel at different speeds through different types of rock. The reflection and refraction of these waves enable them to be recorded at the surface and eventually a pattern of the rock formations underground may be drawn. Reflection surveys are the most popular geophysical method used. Geophones are positioned in a straight line through the explosion point and the time taken for the waves from the explosion to reach the geophone after reflection from the rocks beneath enables the underlying structure to be mapped after repeated surveys are made in the area.

Seismic surveying at sea is much easier than on land as the geophones may be towed behind one vessel while another detonates the explosion just below the surface. No time-consuming drilling of boreholes is necessary nor the careful laying out of geophones by hand as must be done on land.

Geochemical methods of detecting oil and gas beneath the surface are also used. These rely on the fact that over millions of years traces of oil will gradually percolate up to the surface and be detectable in the soil. In practice only very minute quantities are found, except in the case of true seepages, and it has been shown that hydrocarbon traces may also be due to plant root remains in the soil. A variation of this idea is an underwater 'seep detector' which is claimed to be able to detect hydrocarbons in sea water and hence indicate areas where oil or gas may be found.

The methods of exploration described so far can pinpoint likely rock formations where oil and gas may have accumulated but the only means of discovering if hydrocarbons are actually present is to drill an exploratory well. There are many ways of obtaining the maximum amount of information from an exploratory well. One of the simplest is by examination of the bit cuttings brought to the surface by the drilling fluid, 'mud'. These cuttings can confirm predictions about the geological structure of the area and can also be analysed for traces of oil or gas. The so-called 'mud' was originally a mixture of clay and water but is now a carefully prepared mixture, consisting essentially of a plastic polymer in suspension in water or oil, and it serves not only to remove the cuttings but also to prevent a 'blow-out' if oil or gas under pressure is found. The exact composition of the mud has to be very carefully controlled to ensure that it is of the correct viscosity and density, and it also gives a useful indication of the presence of hydrocarbons in a reservoir. Oil may be seen as dark spots in the mud or as a film on the surface as the mud settles. Similarly, gas may be seen as bubbles in the mud as it reaches the surface. Before either oil or gas may be seen in the mud, it can, of course, be detected instrumentally.

Another important source of information during drilling is the examination of cores which show the nature of the rock being drilled. The use of a coring bit, which is essentially a hollow tube with a cutting edge, slows the progress of the well, but in exploratory wells in new areas of interest a core 20 ft (6·1 m) long is taken in every 50 ft (15·2 m) drilled. There are also special drilling bits with which a small pencil of core may be obtained through a small hole without slowing the progress of drilling. The cores are tested for the presence of hydrocarbons and the rocks are tested for porosity and permeability.

Once a well has been drilled instruments may be lowered down the hole and be used to transmit valuable information about the physical properties of the rocks. Measurements made in this way include resistivity of the rock, electrochemical potentials and radioactivity of the surrounding formations.

If oil or gas is found under considerable pressure the mud may be used to seal the well temporarily or to control the output of gas or oil while tests on its composition are made. Once a find of gas or oil has been established the extent of the field is determined by drilling 'step-out' wells around the original wells. In some cases several oil or gas fields formed at different times are found directly beneath one another. Due to the different age of the reservoirs the oil in them often varies considerably in type. Although wells have been drilled which tap all the fields through one set of wells it is more usual for each field to be produced separately by a set of wells to that field only, as this gives better control of production. Where oil and gas are found together it is often possible by careful siting of wells to produce oil from one well and gas from another although it will often be found in such cases that a considerable amount of gas is dissolved in the oil.

Production

Many of the techniques of drilling for and recovering gas were developed originally for oil, but in the case of gas beneath the North Sea a new type of drilling rig had to be developed to work in the sea under what are sometimes very adverse conditions. Gas had to be handled at high pressures and techniques had to be adapted from those in use in the chemical industry. For hundreds of years wells for oil were dug by hand in Burma. This method was slow and dangerous for the digger especially as the depth increased when the time he could safely stay down decreased rapidly. In about 1900 an air supply of a kind was introduced to help the digger as he approached the oil but by about 1910 this method of digging wells was dying out.

By the late eighteenth century in Europe and America a method of drilling by means of a bit suspended from a wooden spring pole and worked like a pile-driver was in use. The cuttings were baled out from time to time. The Chinese had used this method two thousand years earlier to drill brine wells to a depth of a thousand feet, the wells being lined with hollow bamboo.

In the middle of the nineteenth century steam engines were first introduced to power the drills and, with other developments such as the use of wire rope and the construction of casing for the well, greatly increased the efficiency of drilling. Using these methods wells of about 3000 ft were successfully completed and brought into production. This depth was later increased as methods of casing and drilling improved, but although the cable method held its own for thirty years after the introduction of rotary drills, it declined in popularity in the 1930s. Rotary drilling had considerable advantages since the circulating 'mud' removed the fragments of rock continuously and also helped to stabilize the walls of the wells making casing less necessary. Progress was also much quicker especially when drilling through soft rocks. An important extension of rotary drilling is turbo-drilling where the bit is rotated by a turbine just above it and the whole drillstring no longer has to rotate with the bit. This has important applications in drilling hard rocks where it is appreciably quicker than a conventional drill and it is also advantageous in directional drilling.

In order to complete a well, the well is cased down to a point at which the oil or gas is present. The gas flows up through an inner pipe which is surrounded by an outer pipe containing 'mud' which can be released to kill the well if this should be necessary.

When wells are to be drilled at sea there are several different types of drilling platform which may be used. These fall into two basic categories, floating and fixed. The floating type consists of drilling ships, which are not very stable in rough seas, and semi-submersible platforms. These platforms are used when the depth of water is too great for fixed rigs but being partly submerged they have considerably greater stability than ships. There are two main types of fixed platform, submersibles which are towed to the well location and then sunk on to the sea bed, and jack-up platforms which reach the drilling site with their legs above the surface of the water but are then fixed by means of jacking down the legs until they reach the sea-bed. The latter type of platform can be moved fairly readily to a new site but the submersibles are permanent and as such are only practical for use on proven fields. The maximum depth of water in which jack-up rigs can operate is about 300 ft and this is the most popular type of rig in use in that part of the North Sea which does not exceed this depth.

The fixing of drilling rigs in such adverse conditions as are often found in the North Sea is not an easy undertaking and the ability to drill several wells from one platform by means of directional drilling is particularly useful. Up to twelve wells may be drilled from one platform, the bottom of a shaft often being a mile distant from the rig. Deviation of the drill pipe is achieved by means of a 'whipstock' or wedge which is inserted at intervals in the drilling process. The direction of drilling is controlled by means

18 *Work on the derrick floor of the drilling rig 'Mr Louie'*

of a gyroscope. The introduction of the turbo-drill has greatly eased the problems of directional drilling since considerably less strain is placed on the system if only the drilling bit needs to rotate.

When a production well has been successfully drilled and the drilling completed the derricks can be removed and the platform ultimately controlled automatically from the shore. The production platforms are often a considerable distance from the shore and sophisticated methods of communication are required to control a platform which is over the horizon.

The gas from the production platform is piped ashore along a pipeline on the seabed. This pipeline is laid using a special barge which actually lays the pipe on the seabed, to be buried in the mud by a 'jetting barge' which uses high pressure water jets to cut a trench into which the pipe sinks. The pipe is coated with glass fibre and pitch or coal-tar enamel and then given a further coating of concrete to help it to sink. The welds are

19 *Model of the North Sea drilling rig 'Orion' (in Science Museum collections)*

examined by x-rays before being coated. The barge moves forward one pipeline length at a time by means of anchors fore and aft and the pipeline passes down a sloping bridge or 'stinger' to the seabed.

Most treatment of the gas is done at the shore terminals but before the gas passes through the submarine pipeline solids must be filtered out and the gas must be dried to avoid formation of methane hydrate at high pressure in the pipeline. This is a snow-like substance which can block the pipe. The preferred methods of removing water are absorption by triethylene glycol/water solution, absorption by solid desiccants or simple refrigeration methods. Alternatively, methanol can be added to the gas at the well-head on the production platform. This inhibits the formation of methane hydrate. A mixed water/methanol condensate forms 'slugs' of liquid in the undersea pipe but this can easily be removed at the shore terminal.

20 *A production platform on the Leman field in the North Sea. The wells were drilled from the platform on the right and on the left some treatment of the gas takes place before it is piped ashore*

The gas from under the North Sea is piped ashore to a terminal at the nearest convenient point; the gas from several fields sometimes being received at a single terminal. The shore terminal is in two main parts, the producer's section and the British Gas Corporation section. The gas enters the producer's section and any 'pigs' or 'slugs' are removed. A 'pig' is a heavy spherical object which can be inserted in the pipeline and is used to clear any condensate in the pipeline between the platform and the terminal. If an appreciable volume of condensate accumulates in the pipeline this comes ashore as a 'slug' to be removed in 'slug catchers' which consist of 100 ft lengths of 30 inch pipe with a 1-in-50 fall. The gas is then dried, products such as butane being removed by fractional distillation and stored separately, and finally metered before going to the Gas Corporation terminal. In the Gas Corporation section the gas is again filtered and then blended to maintain a standard quality and thermal content. The gas needs to be heated in the terminal to prevent ice forming on the equipment since the gas is drastically cooled due to expansion when its pressure is reduced. The gas is usually odourless and therefore as a safety precaution 'smell' is added to it before its distribution. Finally the gas is metered using orifice meters mounted in the very large pipes and is then supplied to the grid.

Storage and distribution of natural gas
The demand for gas varies considerably depending on the time of year,

21 *The storage of liquid natural gas at Glenmavis in Scotland*

the day and even the time of day. Natural gas therefore has to be stored at times of low demand for use at peak periods. For very local, small-scale storage to cope with daily variations the conventional gasholders are used, but other types of storage are necessary for most of the gas to cover the very large differences in seasonal demand.

Natural gas, being predominantly methane, has a great advantage over town gas, (which is mainly hydrogen, and has a very low boiling point), as it may be readily liquefied for transport and storage. If gas is stored in liquid form six hundred times as much may be stored in a certain volume as would be possible if it were in gaseous form. Several types of storage have been used including double-shelled insulated cylindrical tanks and frozen ground units. The latter were formed by freezing a cylindrical shape in the earth, excavating the central core and then filling the cavity with liquid gas. The unit was covered by an insulated gas-right roof which was provided with a boil-off vent.

Storage of gas in the gaseous state in large quantities is often achieved by using underground geological formations. Depleted gas or oil fields can be recharged with gas. Similar structures (aquifers) which have never actually contained gas can be used by pumping in gas to replace the water in the rock. Aquifers are used in many parts of the world but not at present in England. Another form of underground storage is in salt cavities; if these are surrounded by impermeable salt the cavity may be used to store gas.

Another potential but at present little-used form of gas storage is within

22 *The compressor station at Alrewas, the first to be built in Britain*

the high-pressure gas grid. Provided that the grid is not being used to capacity an increase of pressure allows effectively for some gas storage.

The pipeline laid in the early 1960s to take natural gas which arrived by tanker at Canvey Island to the different area boards, formed the basis of the now countrywide high-pressure gas grid. All twelve areas are served by the grid which is now fed by gas from the North Sea via the shore terminals on the east coast. In the 1970s the pressure in the grid was kept within the range 550-1000 lbs/sq in (approximately 35-70 atmospheres). The pipeline is in general 36 inches in diameter, although in other countries even larger pipe has been laid.

When the new main was laid the welding of the pipes was checked by x-rays to give maximum reliability, and the pipeline was buried in trenches. Great efforts were made to restore the landscape to its original state once the pipe had been laid. In order to maintain the high pressure in the mains, however, booster stations have to be sited about every 40 miles (64 km) and also at branches in the network. These stations are powered by gas using very large gas turbines similar to aero engines, efficiently sound-proofed.

The existence of a countrywide grid has great environmental advantages since many local gasworks have been replaced with a few shore terminals where maximum efforts have been made to landscape the necessary plant.

The gas from the high-pressure grid can be stored in the separate regions in high-pressure holders, or after pressure reduction by governors, in conventional gasholders for local use. In all areas local pipe systems were, of course, already in existence for town gas and formed the local distribution system for natural gas.

Flames and the conversion programme
When a gas burns chemical reactions occur in the flame between the

components of the gas and the air or oxygen in which it is burning. These reactions release the energy stored in the gas and this may be seen as the light emitted by some flames and felt as the heat given out. Some gases such as hydrogen burn with a flame which produces very little light, and it was only the presence of impurities such as ethylene and acetylene which enabled town gas to be used for lighting in the early nineteenth century before the introduction of incandescent mantles.

Most of the early gas-burners produced diffusion flames. These flames burnt by drawing in air at the edges of the flame and the gas only burns in this region. This type of burner tended to produce soot as the gas was often incompletely burnt. The premixed flame was a great improvement on the diffusion flame as in burners producing it air is mixed with the gas below the point of combustion. The premixed flame is the most favoured type of burner design as combustion is efficient and the maximum amount of heat is obtained from the gas.

Different gases have different burning characteristics so that when it was decided to change from a town gas (mainly hydrogen) to a natural gas (methane) system gas appliances had to be converted to burn methane as efficiently as possible. The calorific value (heating capacity) of natural gas is approximately double that of town gas, so that in order to produce the same amount of heat in a given time, only half as much gas is needed. However, this smaller volume of gas still requires slightly more air than that needed to burn the original, larger, volume of town gas. In order to obtain the correct mixture of air and gas the natural gas is supplied to the burner at a higher pressure than town gas but through a smaller orifice, resulting in more air being drawn in but keeping the overall volume constant.

Different gases burn at different speeds. Town gas burns much faster than natural gas due to its higher hydrogen content. As a result of this difference further adjustments have been made to town gas burners to prevent the natural gas flames lifting off the burner ports. This is done by introducing an extra 'retention' flame from a very small burner just below the main burner which prevents the main flame from lifting off, and thereby becoming very unstable and easily extinguished.

The conversion from town gas to natural gas in Great Britain was the largest exercise of its type ever undertaken anywhere in the world. Forty million appliances were converted, including many different models of each type of appliance; for example, a thousand different designs of cooker were converted. Such an exercise would never be repeated. If gas-making again becomes necessary at some future time, the gas would probably be made from coal by processes developed by the British gas industry. In the mid 1970s, some areas which had been converted but awaited being linked to the natural gas transmission network were supplied with substitute natural gas made in a process developed by the British gas industry.

Special uses of natural gas

With the advent of natural gas many new applications of gas for heating and other processes have become possible due to its purity, the increased quantity available and the ease with which it can be distributed.

The absence of sulphur compounds in natural gas is particularly advantageous in the glass and ceramics industries where it is essential that the combustion products do not affect the quality of the product. Natural gas is also used as a fuel in steel-making and iron foundries, where the capacity of blast furnaces can be increased by as much as 25%. Research is going on into the possible use of the carbon in the methane of natural gas as the source of carbon for steel manufacture instead of coke.

Natural gas can be used very efficiently to drive internal combustion engines, but until comparatively recently the problems of storage meant that its use was primarily for stationary engines. However, storage cylinders suitable for installation in a car or truck have been developed and results of experiments have been very favourable. Natural gas has been tested in vehicles using petrol as a standby fuel and there was a considerable decrease in the amount of undesirable exhaust gases produced.

A prototype fuel cell using natural gas has been produced in the United States of America and has been operated for over 2,000 hours with no reduction in performance. Fuel cells of this type have been installed experimentally to assess their possible commercial use.

Many large-scale gas users such as power stations have dual fuel systems which enable them to buy gas at favourable terms under an interruptible contract but which requires them to switch to an alternative fuel (usually oil) at a few hours notice if requested to do so by the gas suppliers. This type of contract enables the gas producers to even out the seasonal fluctuations in gas demand and to have additional gas available at a few hours notice in case of emergencies or exceptionally high demand.

Another important use of gas as a fuel is in total energy systems in which a large area ranging from a block of flats to a complex comprising shops, offices and houses is supplied with a single source of energy from which all demands for power are met. In such a system gas can be used to provide space-heating, hot water and air-conditioning, and also to generate electricity using gas turbines. Energy is much more efficiently used than in the conventional provision of power.

Natural gas is an important chemical feedstock. Although most North Sea gas is virtually free of sulphur compounds, natural gas in other parts of the world contains considerable amounts in the form of hydrogen sulphide. Removal of this impurity in the form of elemental sulphur provides a useful by-product. Natural gas is also used for the production of carbon black, the gas being burnt in a limited supply of air and the product deposited on a cool surface. The carbon black is used in the manufacture of printing ink, polishes, varnishes and motor tyres.

A considerable proportion of the world's output of ammonia is produced from natural gas by a catalytic process. The ammonia produced is used as a plant food and also as a secondary feedstock for the production of hydrogen cyanide, nitric acid, urea and several fertilisers. Natural gas is also widely used as a feedstock for the production of synthesis gas (hydrogen and carbon monoxide) as a starting point for the manufacture of plastics.

There has been considerable research into synthesising protein micro-biologically using petroleum compounds which provide a ready source of carbon atoms. These experiments led to the production of protein concentrates and it is possible that natural gas could also be used in this way. A large-scale pilot plant has shown a very promising yield of protein from natural gas. The advantage of using gas would be that the product should be uncontaminated by other hydrocarbons. The nitrogen for the proteins comes from the air. If these experiments are successful there are countries which are rich in gas but poor in protein which could benefit considerably from such a utilisation of their excess gas.

Printed in England for Her Majesty's Stationery Office by
W & J Mackay Limited, Chatham

Dd 496454 K64 4/76